ALAN CRADDOCK '83

SUPERMAN

ANNUAL 198

D1060709

£2.75

ROCKETED AS A BABY FROM THE DOOMED PLANET KRYPTON, *KAL-EL* REACHED EARTH, WHOSE ENVIRONMENT GAVE HIM SUPER-POWERS. POSING AS MILD-MANNERED NEWSMAN *CLARK KENT*, HE FIGHTS EVIL AS...

SUPERMAN®

Created by JERRY SIEGEL & JOE SHUSTER

BOTH ON HER HOMEWORLD THANAGAR, IN THE STAR-SYSTEM OF POLARIS, AND ON THE PLANET EARTH, *SHAYERA* HAS BEEN BOTH MATE AND PARTNER-AGAINST-CRIME OF HER HUSBAND, *KATAR HOL*, THE *HAWKMAN*. WHEN DANGERS LOOM AGAINST THE SUN, SHE SOARS TO MEET THEM AS THE HIGH-FLYING...

HAWKGIRL™

NOW, *KRYPTONIAN* AND *THANAGARIAN* JOIN FORCES, IN THE ADVENTURE--

THE STARS, LIKE MOTHS...!

JIM STARLIN
plot & art

ROY THOMAS
script

GENE D'ANGELO
colors

COSTANZA
letters

JULIUS SCHWARTZ
editor

From the *docu-diary* of *SHAYERA*, a.k.a. *SHIERA HALL* (FINAL ENTRY):

"...AND *STILL* THEY MOVE INEXORABLY, IRRESISTIBLY INWARD, THOSE GREAT ROCK-LIKE FRAGMENTS OF WORLDS LONG DEAD...

"...DRAWN LIKE SOFT-WINGED *INSECTS* TOWARD THAT BLINDING RED LIGHT WHICH IS, IN TRUTH, *DEATH*.

"*THEY* WILL NOT *DIE*, THESE STAR-SHARDS...FOR THEY HAVE NOT *LIFE* TO LOSE.

"BUT THE BRIGHTLY-CLAD *SON* OF LOST KRYPTON WHO CLINGS TO ONE OF THEM, AS IF TO *EXISTENCE* ITSELF...HE *CAN* DIE, AND SO SOON HE *SHALL*...!

S-3602

"YET, THIS TRAGEDY--WHICH MAY SOON BE MY *OWN,* AS WELL--BEGAN AS SO MANY EPOCH-MAKING EVENTS ON THE PLANET EARTH DO: WITH A TELEPHONE CALL...

RRRINNG

HELLO, THIS IS *DR. IRWIN WRIGHT,* OF THE CENTER FOR AMERINDIAN STUDIES... I'M CALLING LONG DISTANCE.

MAY I SPEAK TO *MR. CARTER HALL,* PLEASE?

I'M SORRY, BUT HE'S... *AWAY.*

THIS IS HIS *WIFE.* MAY I HELP YOU?

UH...I'M AFRAID, MRS. HALL, THAT WHAT I'M CALLING ABOUT REQUIRES SOMEONE OF HIS, ER, *SPECIALIZED KNOWLEDGE.*

I'M NOT A MUSEUM DIRECTOR, BUT I'VE WORKED WITH MY HUSBAND!

VERY WELL, THEN...

I'M SURE I CAN RELY UPON YOU TO *COMMUNICATE* WHAT I'M ABOUT TO TELL YOU TO *MR. HALL.*

I'LL DO MY *BEST!*

I'M CALLING FROM A HOUSE I'VE RENTED, IN THE *ROCKY MOUNTAINS...*

IN PERFORMING SOME *ARCHEOLOGICAL EXCAVATIONS* NEARBY, I BELIEVE I'VE UNCOVERED SOME *ARTIFACTS* WHICH ARE...UH... *NOT OF EARTHLY ORIGIN.*

I, ER, KNOW THIS MAY SOUND *LAUGHABLE,* BUT--

I'M *NOT* LAUGHING, DR. WRIGHT.

THANK YOU FOR *THAT.*

I'LL LEAVE MY ADDRESS AND PHONE NUMBER, AS I BELIEVE IT *IMPORTANT* THAT YOUR HUSBAND GET IN TOUCH WITH ME AS SOON AS *POSSIBLE!*

OF *COURSE,* SIR... AS SOON AS POSSIBLE.

GOOD-BYE.

YES, DR. WRIGHT... ...ONE OF US *WILL* BE WITH YOU, ON THE EARLIEST AVAILABLE...

...*FLIGHT!*

"WHAT FOOLS THESE EARTHMEN BE... TO PARAPHRASE ONE OF THEIR OWN MORE PERCEPTIVE POETS.

"BUT PERHAPS I'M BEING UNFAIR, SINCE THE GOOD PROFESSOR COULDN'T HAVE KNOWN THAT, AS ONE ORIGINALLY SENT TO THIS PLANET TO STUDY CERTAIN ASPECTS OF ITS PEOPLE, I KNOW MORE ABOUT ARCHEOLOGY THAN MOST OF ITS PH.D.'S.

"AT ANY RATE, AFTER LEAVING A NOTE FOR CARTER, WHO'D BE IN CAIRO FOR SEVERAL MORE DAYS, I WAS SOON WINGING MY WAY WESTWARD FROM MIDWAY CITY...

"...WITH A SINGLE CHANGE OF CLOTHES.

YOUR HOUSEKEEPER TOLD ME I'D FIND YOU HERE ON YOUR "DIG". DR. WRIGHT?

MY HUSBAND COULDN'T MAKE IT, BUT I'M SHIERA HALL, AND--

BUT... I-I REALLY WANTED--

I ASSURE YOU I CAN RECOGNIZE ARTIFACTS OF THE UTO-AZTECAN AND YUMAN CULTURES QUITE AS READILY AS MY HUSBAND CAN!

I ALSO READ EGYPTIAN HIEROGLYPHS AND ASSYRO-BABYLONIAN CUNEIFORM, IF IT COMES TO THAT. HMMM...

I'M SORRY IF I SOUND OLD-FASHIONED, MRS. HALL. IT'S JUST THAT WHAT I FOUND IN THE CHAMBER I'VE UNCOVERED... WELL, IT'S RATHER UPSET ME.

NO APOLOGIES NECESSARY.

YOU SEE, I'VE READ SO MANY ARTICLES UNDER MR. HALL'S BYLINE IN THE AMERICAN GEOGRAPHIC...

WE WRITE THEM TOGETHER... BUT I'M PUBLICITY-SHY.

THEN PERHAPS YOU ARE THE ONE TO MAKE SOME SENSE--

--OUT OF THIS!

GOOD HEAVENS!

YOU SHARE MY AMAZEMENT, THEN?

THAT I DO! NOT ONLY IS THIS CHAMBER DISTINCTLY UN-INDIAN...

...BUT THIS INSCRIPTION LOOKS LIKE NO LANGUAGE ON EARTH!

AND I KNOW WHAT I'M TALKING ABOUT!

NO, I CAN'T READ IT, DR. WRIGHT... AND NEITHER, I'M POSITIVE, COULD MY HUSBAND.

BUT I THINK I MAY JUST KNOW SOMEONE WHO CAN!

THIS IS AN EVEN MORE INCREDIBLE FIND THAN WRIGHT IMAGINES!

I'M CERTAIN THIS WRITING IS KRYPTONESE-- THE LANGUAGE OF THE LONG-DEAD PLANET KRYPTON!

IN SHORT, AND CORNY AS IT MAY SOUND... THIS LOOKS LIKE A JOB FOR SUPERMAN!

"AFTER NIGHTFALL, WHEN I'D MANAGED TO TALK DR. WRIGHT INTO LEAVING ME ALONE WITH HIS PRECIOUS FIND...

"...THE SUDDEN FLUTTERING OF A LAMP-FLAME ALERTED ME...

"...THAT I WAS NOT ALONE:

YOU SENT FOR ME, SHAY --UH, HAWKGIRL?

YOU CAN MAKE IT SHAYERA...

I'M DOWN HERE.

I APPRECIATE YOUR COMING SO QUICKLY WHEN I COULD FINALLY CONTACT YOU VIA THE JLA SIGNAL.

I TRUST YOU CAN SEE WHY I CALLED!

TAKE A LOOK AROUND--THEN YOU TELL ME!

IS THIS REALLY-- WHAT IT SEEMS TO BE?

I COULDN'T SEE IN HERE AS I FLEW IN, BECAUSE THERE'S LEAD IN THE WALLS.

...BUT NOW-- THIS INSCRIPTION! IT'S A MESSAGE OF WELCOME, IN THE NATIVE TONGUE OF KRYPTON!

I SUSPECTED AS MUCH.

STILL, THERE'S SOMETHING ODD ABOUT IT.

REALLY? I BARELY RECOGNIZED IT AS KRYPTONESE--FROM WHEN KATAR AND I VISITED YOUR FORTRESS OF SOLITUDE.

SO YOU HAD NO WAY OF KNOWING THAT THE MESSAGE IS WRITTEN IN A STYLE AND SYNTAX-- THAT'S MORE THAN A HUNDRED YEARS OLD!

WHAT?!

YES. THIS IS A KRYPTONIAN WELCOMING ROOM-- AN ANTECHAMBER, SO TO SPEAK.

YOU MEAN-- THERE'S MORE TO THIS PLACE?

7

CONSIDERABLY MORE.

RIGHT...

...BEHIND...

...HERE!

STILL HAVE THAT FAMOUS KRYPTONIAN *LIGHT TOUCH*, I SEE!

WHOMP!

WELCOME TO *SOMEBODY'S* SANCTUM SANCTORUM, SHAYERA.

IT'S-- *UNBELIEVABLE*--

--A WHOLE *KRYPTONIAN LABORATORY*, MUCH LIKE THE ONE WE SAW IN YOUR ARCTIC *FORTRESS!*

I CAN SEE WHY YOU WERE ONE OF THE MOST SUCCESSFUL *POLICE OFFICERS* BACK ON YOUR NATIVE *THANAGAR!*

AND YET-- I DON'T KNOW-- IT SEEMS *DIFFERENT*, IN SOME SUBTLE WAY.

YES, THERE *IS* SOMETHING STRANGE ABOUT THIS PLACE...

...THE SAME THING THAT WAS STRANGE ABOUT THE *INSCRIPTION* OUTSIDE.

YOU MEAN-- ITS *AGE?*

YES-- AND *NO!* IT'S DEFINITELY A KRYPTONIAN LAB OF NEARLY A *CENTURY* BEFORE THE PLANET EXPLODED--

--AND, AT THE SAME TIME, IN MANY WAYS IT SEEMS *EVEN MORE ADVANCED* THAN THE ONE MY FATHER, *JOR-EL*, HAD!

8

ARE YOU SAYING IT'S BOTH *FUTURISTIC*-- AND *QUAINT?*

NOT IN *YOUR* EYES, OF COURSE ...OR TO THOSE OF BORN *EARTHMEN*... BUT TO ME, IT'S LIKE SOMETHING OUT OF AN OLD *JULES VERNE* NOVEL.

HMMM... THIS OLD-FASHIONED *PROJECTRON* MAY GIVE US SOME ANSWERS.

IT'S AN EARLY TYPE OF THREE-DIMENSIONAL *RECORDER* THAT--

LOOK! AN *IMAGE*-- FORMING ABOVE THE GRID!

IT'S-- *HIM!*

YOU *KNOW* THE MAN *WHO* GOES WITH THAT FACE?

NO, I NEVER REALLY *KNEW* HIM,... AND YET, I SAW HIS IMAGE *COUNTLESS* TIMES WHEN I WAS AN INFANT BACK ON KRYPTON!

THAT'S *VAR-EL*... MY *GREAT-GRANDFATHER!*

YOUR--?

THAT'S RIGHT-- MY OWN *ANCESTOR*, A SCIENTIST OF WHOM VERY LITTLE IS KNOWN--

--BECAUSE HE *DISAPPEARED* WITHOUT A TRACE, LONG BEFORE I WAS BORN!

THEN PERHAPS THE *PROJECTRON* CAN TELL YOU WHAT *HAPPENED* TO HIM.

THAT'S WHAT I'M HOPING!

APPARENTLY, NO ONE'S *PLAYED* THIS PRO-JECTA-TAPE SINCE IT WAS MADE, SO I'LL JUST *REWIND* IT.

THERE! NOW TO SEE WHAT MY FAMOUS FOREBEAR HAS TO *SAY* FOR HIMSELF...

HUH? I *STILL* DON'T UNDERSTAND *KRYPTONESE.*

THAT'S WHY I SENT FOR *YOU* IN THE FIRST PLACE, REMEMBER?

SORRY ABOUT THAT! LUCKILY, I CAN SET THE MACHINE TO *TRANSLATE* MY GREAT-GRAND-FATHER'S MESSAGE, AS WELL.

BUT--WHAT DID HE *SAY?*

JUST ENOUGH FOR ME TO KNOW THAT THIS IS HIS *SCIENTIFIC JOURNAL.*

NOW, WE CAN -BOTH FIND OUT *TOGETHER*--

--WHAT A *KRYPTONIAN* WAS DOING ON EARTH-- IN THE *MIDDLE 1800'S!*

...have been on this planet which its inhabitants call EARTH, for several of its YEARS.

At last, I have made progress in testing my long-held theory of a UNIVERSAL SOLAR ENERGIES STORAGE SYSTEM...

...which I was FORBIDDEN to test on my native KRYPTON.

Since KRYPTON has not yet developed interplanetary travel, I devised my own secret TELEPORTATION DEVICE...

...which sent me across the cosmos in an INSTANT, to a planet not only well-suited to my PURPOSE...

...but inhabited, as well.

Fortunately, I soon realized its people couldn't HARM me, even if they discovered my presence...

For I have tremendous powers of strength and FLYING and INVULNERABILITY, under Earth's yellow sun...

...all of which made it far easier to build and equip my hidden LABORATORY!

I have spent years now testing my theory, always fearful that the powers-that-be of KRYPTON might somehow find me here and try to stop me.

DID YOU HEAR THAT, SUPERMAN?

SOUNDS AS IF YOUR ANCESTOR CAME HERE TO PERFORM ILLEGAL SCIENTIFIC TESTS HE COULDN'T DO BACK HOME!

THEN HE'S NEITHER THE FIRST NOR THE LAST TO DO SUCH A THING, SHAYERA.

LOOK AT ALL THE SCIENTISTS NOW DOING GENETIC RESEARCH IN FOREIGN COUNTRIES BECAUSE THE U.S. WON'T ALLOW THEM TO PERFORM THEIR EXPERIMENTS HERE.

BUT LISTEN--THERE'S MORE--!

At last, I have created a COSMIC IRIS by means of which I can monitor the dimension which must exist, if my theory is correct.

Now, I shall TEST it...

...and if RAO is kind, my NEXT ENTRY shall tell of the RESULTS...and of what they may portend for humankind the UNIVERSE over!

AND THAT'S WHERE THE JOURNAL...ENDS.

BUT, EXCEPT FOR TELLING US HOW HE CAME HERE...IT TOLD US NOTHING.

ON THE CONTRARY, HAWKGIRL, IT TOLD ME...NEARLY EVERYTHING!

WHAT--?!

I LEARNED WHAT LITTLE WAS KNOWN OF *VAR-EL* FROM MY UNCLE *ZOR-EL*, IN KANDOR!

VAR VANISHED SOON AFTER THE *SCIENCE COUNCIL* REFUSED TO LET HIM CONTINUE EXPERIMENTATION ON THAT *THEORY* THE *PROJECTA-TAPE* MENTIONED.

HIS THEORY WAS THAT *ALL ENERGY* IS NATURALLY *ATTRACTED* TO ITSELF, AND TO OTHER ENERGY... AND THAT NOT EVEN *DIMENSIONAL BARRIERS* PROVE ANY OBSTACLE TO THAT ATTRACTION.

VAR-EL THOUGHT, FOR INSTANCE, THAT THE ENERGY OF *EXPLODING STARS* PASSES INTO A CERTAIN *"X-DIMENSION."*.. FOR COLD STORAGE, YOU MIGHT SAY.

FROM THERE, IT OCCASIONALLY *EMERGES*... TO AID IN THE CREATION OF A *NEW* STAR.

THAT THEORY WOULD RATHER MAKE *MINCEMEAT* OF EINSTEIN'S $E=MC^2$, WOULDN'T IT?

MAYBE *NOT.* AS I RECALL, MY GREAT-GRANDFATHER'S THEORY TOOK THAT INTO *CONSIDERATION* SOMEHOW.

THIS CLEARS UP *ONE* MYSTERY THAT'S BOTHERED ME ALL MY LIFE, THOUGH.

HOW *MY* FATHER FIRST LEARNED ABOUT *EARTH,* SO THAT HE COULD SEND ME HERE, YEARS LATER!

WHICH IS--?

IF FATHER SAW *OTHER* JOURNALS LIKE THIS ONE, THEN *VAR-EL* IS RESPONSIBLE FOR MY *BEING* HERE... BEING *ANYWHERE,* REALLY!

WHAT DO YOU SUPPOSED HAPPENED TO VAR-EL?

I... DON'T KNOW. UH, WOULD YOU MIND LEAVING ME FOR A FEW MINUTES, SHAYERA?

I'D LIKE TO BE *ALONE,* TO EXAMINE THE LAB THOROUGHLY.

SURE THING! I WANT TO BRING IN SOME OF DR. WRIGHT'S *EQUIPMENT,* ANYWAY.

"THE NEXT MOMENT, SOMETHING DETACHED ITSELF FROM THE GLOOMY SHADOWS TO LEAP HEADLONG AT ME... SOMETHING *HUGE*, MENACING..."

GRARRRGK

GREAT STARS! WHAT--?

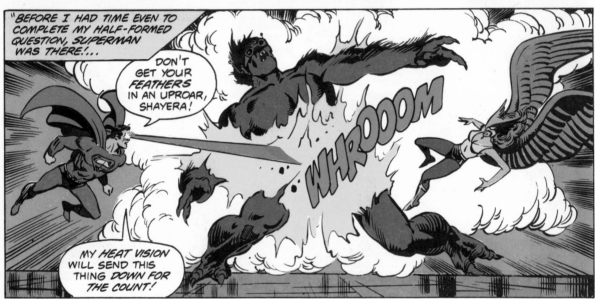

"BEFORE I HAD TIME EVEN TO COMPLETE MY HALF-FORMED QUESTION, SUPERMAN WAS THERE!..."

DON'T GET YOUR *FEATHERS* IN AN UPROAR, SHAYERA!

WHROOOM

MY *HEAT VISION* WILL SEND THIS THING *DOWN FOR THE COUNT!*

THANKS, FRIEND!

I GUESS *NOW* WE KNOW WHAT HAPPENED TO *VAR-EL*, EH?

NO, I DON'T THINK SO...

THIS WAS A KRYPTONIAN *ROBOT*, MADE OF MATERIAL FOUND ON *EARTH*... AND THUS UNDOUBTEDLY MADE BY MY ANCESTOR!

FURTHERMORE, IT ONLY ATTACKED YOU, A *NON-KRYPTONIAN*, NOT ME!

NO, I THINK WHAT WE HAVE HERE IS VAR-EL'S HAND-MADE *"WATCH-DOG"*, STILL TRYING TO GUARD THE PLACE AFTER MORE THAN A *CENTURY!*

WELL, *WHATEVER* IT WAS... I *OWE* YOU ONE!

DON'T WORRY ABOUT IT.

"I CAN EASILY *PIECE TOGETHER* WHAT OCCURRED NEXT: AN *INVENTORY*...

IT'S HARD TO KNOW WHERE TO START-- ESPECIALLY SINCE, COME TOMORROW, THIS *DR. WRIGHT* WILL UNDOUBTEDLY WANT TO PORE OVER THE PLACE ON HIS *OWN*.

HMMM... THIS LITTLE GIZMO SEEMS TO DEAL WITH THE *OPERATION* OF THE MONITOR-IRIS DEVISED BY VAR-EL.

MIGHT AS WELL START WITH *IT*...

... SINCE I DON'T KNOW PRECISELY *WHERE* THAT COSMIC IRIS *IS*.

"YET, AT THE PRESSING OF A *BUTTON*...

THE *MONITOR-IRIS!* IT WAS HIDDEN BEHIND THAT *SECTION* OF WALL THAT JUST SLID BACK!

IT STILL *EXISTS*, THEN!

BUT MAYBE IT *DIDN'T WORK*, SO VAR-EL ABANDONED HIS EXPERIMENTS HERE, AND WENT TO STILL *ANOTHER* PLANET.

THEN AGAIN, MAYBE HE *DISCOVERED* SOMETHING BY WATCHING THE MONITOR-- SOMETHING THAT MADE HIM *FLEE!*

WELL, MIGHT AS WELL *TEST* IT WHILE HAWKGIRL'S *OUTSIDE*... AND HOPEFULLY OUT OF HARM'S WAY.

"NO DOUBT, SUPERMAN'S HANDS RAN OVER THE MONITOR KEYS *THOUSANDS* OF TIMES, IN THE SPACE OF MERE SECONDS...

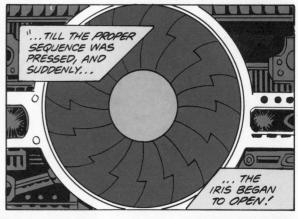

"...TILL THE *PROPER SEQUENCE* WAS PRESSED, AND SUDDENLY...

...THE IRIS BEGAN TO OPEN!

THIS IS FANTASTIC-- *UNBELIEVABLE!*

IT'S LIKE A *WINDOW* ON A *PARALLEL WORLD*-- AN *ALTERNATE UNIVERSE*, WHICH EVEN *I'VE* NEVER SEEN BEFORE! IT--

HUH?

WHAT'S *THAT?!*

MOONS OF KRYPTON! IT-- IT *CAN'T* BE--!

"SECONDS LATER, I DROPPED EVERYTHING BUT MY MACE, AS--

THAT TERRIBLE ROARING SOUND-- COMING FROM THE ANTECHAMBER!

I WANT TO HONOR SUPERMAN'S DESIRE FOR PRIVACY.

STILL, MAYBE HE CAN USE A HAND WITH SOMETHING HE--

WAIT! WHAT'S THAT FORCE-- TUGGING AT ME?

IT'S LIKE-- SOME HORRIBLY STRONG SUCTION THAT-- NO!

IT'S NOT ANY KIND OF SUCTION WIND--

IT'S A GRAVITY PULL!

ONLY--IT'S NOT PULLING ME DOWN-- BUT SIDEWAYS!

LUCKILY, I CAN NEUTRAL- IZE MOST OF ITS EFFECTS-- WITH MY ANTI-GRAVITY BELT!

LIKE THE ADS SAY-- "DON'T LEAVE HOME WITHOUT IT!"

ESPECIALLY SINCE IT'S WHAT ENABLES ME TO FLY!

THERE! THAT SHOULD PROTECT ME, AT LEAST TILL I GET INSIDE.

SUPERMAN! ARE YOU ALL--?

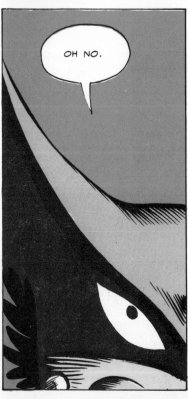

OH NO.

THE *COSMIC IRIS*-- IT'S *WIDE OPEN*, AND EXERTING THE *GRAVITY PULL* I FELT!

THEN, VAR-EL *DIDN'T* INTEND IT TO BE JUST A *WINDOW* ON THE *X-DIMENSION* AT ALL!

OR, IF HE *DID*-- IT DIDN'T *WORK OUT* THAT WAY!

IT'S MORE LIKE AN *OPEN DOORWAY*--

--AND SOMEHOW, DESPITE HIS POWERS-- SUPERMAN'S BEEN *SUCKED INSIDE!*

HE MUST BE IN THERE, SOMEHOW, AMONG ALL THOSE *PLANETARY FRAGMENTS* I CAN SEE !

LIKE THEM, HE'S BEING PROPELLED TOWARD THAT *GIANT, THROBBING LIGHT-SOURCE*, WHICH RESEMBLES A HUGE *RED SUN*--

-- BUT WHICH MUST ACTUALLY BE THE *SUM* OF ALL THE *STELLAR ENERGY* THAT'S ENTERED THE *X-DIMENSION* FOR *BILLIONS OF YEARS!*

"...THAT VAR-EL MISCALCULATED SOMEHOW, AND WAS DRAWN THROUGH THE IRIS TO HIS DOOM, BEFORE HE COULD PROTECT HIMSELF!"

"RIGHT ABOUT NOW, THEN, THE MAN OF STEEL MUST BE FIGURING OUT WHAT HAPPENED TO HIS ANCESTOR..."

"BUT HOW? AFTER ALL, SUPERMAN'S VULNERABLE ONLY TO KRYPTONITE AND CERTAIN KINDS OF MAGIC.

"NO--WAIT! OF COURSE! WE KNOW HE GETS HIS POWER UNDER A YELLOW SUN, LIKE EARTH'S!

"BUT THE X-DIMENSION DRAINS OFF ENERGY FROM ALL EXPLODING STARS--INCLUDING RED ONES, WHICH SAP HIS STRENGTH! AND THE CORE ITSELF IS RED!"

"THAT'S THE FATAL ERROR VAR-EL MUST HAVE MADE, WHICH COST HIM HIS LIFE--

"--AND NOW MAY CLAIM THAT OF HIS DESCENDANT AS WELL!"

"SUPERMAN MAY STILL BE ALIVE--BECAUSE THE YELLOW SUN-SHARDS WILL GIVE BACK SOME OF THE POWERS WHICH THE RED ONES TAKE AWAY...

"HE MAY EVEN HAVE MANAGED TO REACH ONE OF THE FLOATING FRAGMENTS I SEE.

"YET, THEY'RE ALL DRIFTING INWARD-- AND EVEN FROM HERE, I CAN TELL THAT THEY BURN LIKE METEORITES WHEN THEY COME WITHIN RANGE OF THE RED-HOT CORE OF THE X-DIMENSION.

"AND, WITH HIS DIMINISHED POWERS, THE SAME THING WILL HAPPEN TO SUPERMAN--"

--UNLESS *I* CAN DO SOMETHING ABOUT IT.

AND I INTEND TO TRY!

THAT'S WHY I'M DICTATING THIS FINAL *DOCU-DIARY* ENTRY, WHICH IS BEING BEAMED BACK HOME TO *MIDWAY CITY.*

OXY-MASK NOW CLICKING INTO PLACE.

IF YOU FIND THIS ENTRY, *KATAR...* AND IF I *DON'T* RETURN...

...ALWAYS REMEMBER THAT I *LOVED* YOU, TO THE *LAST...*

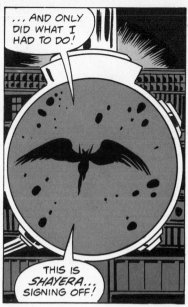

...AND ONLY DID WHAT I HAD TO DO!

THIS IS *SHAYERA...* SIGNING OFF!

THIS IS SHEER *MADNESS*-- AND *FUTILITY!*

EVEN IF I'VE GOT SPEED ENOUGH TO REACH *SUPERMAN* IN TIME--*IF* HE'S NOT ALREADY BEEN *VAPORIZED*-- HOW CAN I HOPE TO *FIND* HIM--

--ONE TINY *MAN,* AMID AN AWESOME, UNFAMILIAR *UNIVERSE?*

GETTING... *WARM!*

WON'T BE LONG NOW, BEFORE THESE *STAR-SHARDS* AND I BOTH TURN INTO *PURE ENERGY...* PART OF THE SHIMMERING CORE OF THIS DIMENSION!

HOLD IT! THAT SOUND *--LIKE THE *BEATING OF WINGS!* COULD IT BE--

--*HAWKGIRL!?*

*Obviously, this dimensional space has some sort of ATMOSPHERE! Otherwise, sound could not travel and the birds could not use their wings!--JULIE

WRONG! IT'S ONE OF THOSE GIGANTIC *SCAVENGER-CREATURES* I'VE SEEN FLYING AROUND!

SOMEHOW, THEY'VE LEARNED TO *LIVE* ON THE EDGE OF THE CORE'S *HOT-WRATH*--

SKRAWNN

--AND NOW THEY'RE COMING FOR *ME!*

17

﹕WHEET WHEET﹕
(STAY BACK, WINGED BROTHERS!)

NO USE! THESE THINGS MAY *LOOK* LIKE BIRDS--AND THEY MAY HAVE LED ME TO *SUPERMAN*--

--BUT THEY *DON'T* RESPOND TO MY *COMMANDS*, AS EARTH BIRDS WOULD! THEY HAVE A DIFFERENT *LANGUAGE!*

IN FACT, THEY'RE EAGER TO MAKE A *MEAL* OF *ME*-- BEFORE THE *CORE-HEAT* HAS A CHANCE AT ME!

WELL, MAYBE MY *INTELLECTUAL CURIOSITY* WILL NEVER BE SATISFIED ABOUT HOW THESE DEVILS *GOT* HERE--OR WHAT THEY *LIVE* ON--

--BUT THIS IS *ONE* TENDER MORSEL THAT *FIGHTS BACK!*

MEANWHILE...

ONE OF THE SCAVENGERS-- *TURNED ASIDE* BACK THERE!

FOR A SECOND, I THOUGHT IT MIGHT BE-- *NO!* MUSTN'T DELUDE MYSELF *AGAIN!*

IF *ANYBODY'S* GOING TO KEEP THESE THINGS FROM DEVOURING ME, LOCK, STOCK, AND *CAPE*--

--IT'S GOT TO BE *YOURS TRULY!*

NOT MUCH-- *STRENGTH* LEFT--

STILL, IF I CAN JUST-- KEEP THE *SHARD*--BETWEEN ME AND *IT*--!

SKRAWW

EH? THEY'RE FLYING AWAY! BUT WHY--?

OF COURSE! THEY FEEL-- THE SAME GROWING, OPPRESSIVE HEAT THAT I DO!

THEY DIDN'T LEAVE-- OUT OF ANY FEAR OF ME-- BUT BECAUSE WE'RE DRIFTING TOO CLOSE TO THE CORE--

--TOO CLOSE-- TO DEATH!

THE STAR-SHARD... IT'S STARTING TO BURN UP...

...JUST AS I ALREADY WOULD HAVE...IF NOT FOR THE YELLOW-SUN ENERGY AROUND!

BUT--THAT WON'T PROTECT ME--FOR LONG.

AFTER ALL THE SUPER-VILLAINS... THE KRYPTONITE... THE MAGIC... WHO'D HAVE THOUGHT IT WOULD END LIKE THIS--

--THAT SUPERMAN WOULD GO OUT-- LIKE A SHOOTING STAR--

--TO BECOME ONE MORE INFINITESIMAL SPECK OF STELLAR ENERGY--

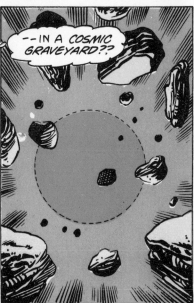

--IN A COSMIC GRAVEYARD??

WHAT'S THAT?!

THE SOUND-- OF WINGS AGAIN!

WELL, COME AND GET ME, BUZZARDS-- IF YOU CAN TAKE THE HEAT!

COME ON AND-- UHHNNNN

GOT HIM-- JUST IN THE PROVERBIAL *NICK!*

ANY CLOSER, AND IT WOULD'VE BEEN *HAWKGIRL* WHO CAUGHT FIRE--INSTEAD OF JUST MY *WINGS!*

GOOD THING THEY LASTED LONG ENOUGH TO CONTROL THE *DIRECTION* OF MY FLIGHT!

NOW, IF MY *ANTI-GRAVITY* SETTING-- CAN JUST PROPEL US BOTH BACK-- THROUGH THE *COSMIC IRIS--!*

PRAISE THANAGAR! IT *DID!*

SORRY FOR THE *ROUGH LANDING,* SUPERMAN.

NEVER MIND ME! JUST-- *SHUT THE IRIS!*

GREAT! IF *RED-SUN* ENERGY HADN'T ESCAPED WHEN IT OPENED, I'D NEVER HAVE BEEN *PULLED IN.*

SOON AS MY *HEAD* STOPS SPINNING, I'M GOING TO *FILL IN* THIS CHAMBER--

-- SO THAT *NO ONE* CAN EVER FALL VICTIM TO THE *X-DIMENSION,* AS MY *ANCESTOR* DID!

THAT'S ONE BURIAL DETAIL I'LL BE *GLAD* TO HELP WITH!

WHAT CAN I *SAY,* SHAYERA...BUT *THANKS?*

FORGET IT! LIKE I SAID... I *OWED* YOU ONE!

JUST DON'T MENTION THIS LITTLE ESCAPADE TO *KATAR,* OKAY--

--TILL I GET A CHANCE TO MAKE UP A *NEW PAIR OF WINGS?*

-END

21

The PREMIERE SHOWING OF A BRAND NEW EPIC STARRING THE ONE AND ONLY

SUPERMAN

MOST EVERYONE KNOWS THAT BEFORE *SUPERMAN* CAME TO *METROPOLIS*, HE SPENT HIS BOYHOOD IN THE TOWN OF *SMALLVILLE!*

YEARS AGO, HE LEFT HIS HOME TOWN FOR THE BIG CITY AND BEGAN HIS ADULT LIFE WORKING FOR THE *DAILY PLANET!* METROPOLIS GAINED A *SUPERMAN--*

--BUT *SMALLVILLE* LOST A *SUPERBOY!* OR *DID* IT? YOU'LL BE ASTONISHED--AND THRILLED --WHEN YOU LEARN THE IDENTITY OF--

"The SECRET GUARDIAN OF SMALLVILLE!"

STORY: CARY BATES
ART: CURT SWAN & BOB OKSNER

S-182B

EDITING: JULIUS SCHWARTZ

22

PART ONE "ENTER THE GUARDIAN..."

ON AN AVERAGE BUSINESS DAY, 4,375 PHONE CALLS COME THROUGH THE *CENTREX COMMUNICATIONS SYSTEM* OF THE *GALAXY BUILDING* IN *METROPOLIS*... BUT ON *THIS* DAY ONLY *ONE* CALL IS OF INTEREST TO A *RED-AND-BLUE* FIGURE STREAKING FROM THE SKY...

RRRRINGG RRRINGG

MY *SUPER-HEARING* WOULD KNOW THAT *DISTINCTIVE RING* ANYWHERE--

--CLARK KENT'S PHONE!

PETE ROSS! GOOD TO HEAR FROM YOU, CHUM!

WHAT'S *NEW?*

BELIEVE IT OR NOT, CLARK, I'M AT THE LOCAL HOTEL IN *SMALLVILLE!* A MUTUAL FRIEND OF OURS *PERSUADED* ME TO COME DOWN HERE!

I'D SURE LIKE YOU TO JOIN ME--HASH OVER THE GOOD OLD DAYS!

WELL, I *DO* HAVE SOME VACATION TIME COMING...

PAL, I'VE GOT THINGS TO TELL YOU ABOUT *YOUR* OLD HOME TOWN YOU WOULDN'T *BELIEVE*--

--BUT I'D RATHER WAIT TILL YOU'RE HERE *IN PERSON!*-- OKAY?

OKAY, PETE, YOU'VE *SOLD* ME!

LOOK FOR ME TO BE DRIVING INTO *SMALLVILLE* BY TONIGHT... OR MORNING!

THINK *PETE ROSS* WOULD BE STARTLED IF HE SAW THAT *SUPERMAN-TO-CLARK KENT* SWITCH, READER? NOT REALLY, BECAUSE...

IT'S TIMES LIKE THIS THAT MAKE ME *GLAD* I KNOW CLARK IS SECRETLY *SUPERMAN!**

NOW... WHATEVER'S GOING ON HERE IN *SMALLVILLE*--HE'LL BE HERE TO HANDLE IT!

*YEARS AGO, A CHANCE ACCIDENT AFFORDED TEEN-AGE *PETE* A GLIMPSE OF *CLARK* SWITCHING TO *SUPERBOY*--A SECRET PETE HAS KEPT FROM THE *MAN OF STEEL* EVER SINCE!--   Editor

LATER THAT NIGHT...

SHUCKS MY STOMACH'S GROWLING FOR A BURGER--BUT I FORGOT *MIDNIGHT* IS THE WRONG TIME TO BE HUNGRY IN THIS TOWN!

SMALLVILLE PULLS IN ITS SIDEWALKS AFTER 10 O'CLOCK!

HOTEL

2

THROUGH BLEARY EYES, PETE WATCHES THE FAMILIAR BUT *OUT-OF-FOCUS* FIGURE OF *RED-AND-BLUE* IN ACTION...

I SHOULD'VE KNOWN -- IF DISASTER STRIKES, CAN GOOD OL' *SUPERMAN* BE FAR BEHIND?

WHAT A GUY! STITCHING UP THE FISSURE WITH A *GIANT NEEDLE* --

-- USING A HEAVY *STEEL CABLE* AS *THREAD!*

PUTTING THE *FINISHING TOUCH* BY FILLING IN THE CRACK WITH *CEMENT*... CLOSING IT UP PERMANENTLY!

POUNDING HEARTBEATS LATER, PETE SEES THE BLURRY, CAPED FIGURE FLY OFF...

THERE HE GOES -- ANOTHER JOB BY *SUPERMAN!*

THE PEOPLE OF *SMALLVILLE* DON'T DREAM HOW *LUCKY* THEY WERE TONIGHT!

4

MORNING, PETER! MY...IT'S LIKE OLD TIMES, SEEING YOU AROUND TOWN AGAIN!

FEELS GOOD TO BE BACK HOME, MRS. SENNETT! SAY HELLO TO YOUR FAMILY FOR ME!

HUH?--THAT'S ODD...NOT A TRACE OF THE FISSURE OR EVEN THE STITCHING!

AFTER I WENT TO BED, SUPERMAN MUST'VE COME BACK AND RE-PAVED THE STREET!

AS FAR AS SMALLVILLE'S CONCERNED, LAST NIGHT'S QUAKE NEVER HAPPENED!

ISN'T THE MIDDLE OF THE STREET A STRANGE PLACE TO BE LOOKING FOR GEOLOGICAL SAMPLES, PAL?

CLARK--!

I DIDN'T HEAR YOU DRIVE UP, OLD BUDDY!

I TRIED TO GET HERE LAST NIGHT...BUT COULDN'T LEAVE METROPOLIS EARLY ENOUGH!

SAME OLD CLARK-- COVERING UP THE FACT HE WAS HERE LAST NIGHT ...AS SUPERMAN!

OKAY, PETE! WHAT'S THE BIG MYSTERY YOU HINTED AT OVER THE PHONE?

AND WHO'S THE MUTUAL FRIEND WHO BROUGHT US TOGETHER AGAIN*?

ONE THING AT A TIME, CLARK! FIRST OF ALL--

*CLARK KENT AND PETE ROSS RECENTLY MET IN "I CAN'T GO HOME AGAIN" IN SUPERMAN #270!-- Editor

--WE'VE GOT SOME FASCINATING RESEARCH TO LOOK INTO!

WHEW! SOMEBODY SURE LEFT THIS LIBRARY REFERENCE ROOM IN A MESS!

FOR YOUR INFORMATION, *MISTER* KENT... THIS *"MESS"* IS THE RESULT OF *LONG HOURS* OF *HARD WORK!*

AND THE *"SOMEBODY"* IS--

--LANA LANG!

WELL, I'LL BE A *MONKEY'S UNCLE!*

GOSH...SO YOU'RE THE MUTUAL FRIEND WHO GOT US TOGETHER!

HI, THERE! LONG TIME NO SEE!

CLARK HASN'T CHANGED-- EVER SO *POLITE*... AND EVER SO *TRITE!*

...AND AFTER I FINISHED MY *OVERSEAS* TELEVISION ASSIGNMENT, SPENDING A FEW WEEKS BACK HOME SEEMED LIKE A GREAT IDEA!

BUT AFTER A COUPLE OF DAYS HERE, I REALIZED SOMETHING WAS *MISSING* FROM THE DAILY EDITION OF THE *SMALLVILLE GAZETTE!*

--NAMELY, *BAD NEWS!* NO MENTION OF A *ROBBERY* OR A *MUGGING*...NOT ONE *FIRE*... NOT SO MUCH AS A SERIOUS *TRAFFIC ACCIDENT!*

AT FIRST I THOUGHT *SMALLVILLE* WAS LEADING A CHARMED LIFE! BUT THEN I DID SOME *DIGGING*...

...AND MY RESEARCH REVEALED THIS REMARKABLE RECORD HAS LASTED FOR *YEARS!*

Circle Cafe

THINK OF IT, CLARK! OVER A *DECADE* WITHOUT A SINGLE *NATURAL DISASTER* OR *SUCCESSFUL CRIME!*

THE FEW CROOKS WHO *DO* TRY TO PULL OFF A JOB ARE *PROMPTLY* AND *MYSTERIOUSLY* CAPTURED!

HERE'S OUR CHANCE TO SEE FOR OURSELVES!-- *LOOK!*

6

GREAT SCOTT! THAT HELICOPTER'S BLASTED A *HOLE* IN THE BANK'S *ROOF!*

A HUGE *MAGNET* HAS LATCHED ONTO THE *SAFE...* PULLING IT *UP!*

SMALLVILLE BANK AND TRUST

SO FAR... *NOTHING'S* STOPPING THOSE *COPTER CROOKS!*

I'VE SEEN THAT *UN-EASY* LOOK ON CLARK'S FACE BEFORE --HE'S *ITCHING* TO SLIP AWAY AND SWITCH TO *SUPERMAN--*

--BUT *WONDERING HOW* TO DO IT WITHOUT AROUSING LANA'S *SUSPICIONS!*

HERE'S WHERE I CAN *HELP OUT* LIKE I USED TO DURING OUR BOYHOOD DAYS!

C'MON, LANA--WE CAN GET A BETTER LOOK FURTHER UP THE STREET!

OHHHHHHH...

AT A CRITICAL TIME LIKE THIS, A GENTLE *NERVE PINCH* IS JUST WHAT THE DOCTOR ORDERED!

WHATTA YA KNOW-- GUESS THE EXCITEMENT WAS TOO MUCH FOR LANA! SHE'S *FAINTED!*

ER...BETTER *STAY* WITH HER, PETE!

I'LL SEE IF I CAN GET SOME HELP!

YEAH... I CAN JUST PICTURE CLARK NOW...

...IN A SECLUDED SPOT... RIPPING OPEN HIS SHIRT AS HE GETS READY TO TACKLE ANOTHER JOB AS *SUPERMAN!*

UP UP AND *AWAY*, AS THE SAYING GOES!

IT SHOULDN'T TAKE MORE THAN A MOMENT TO INTERCEPT AND GROUND THOSE *SAFE-JACKERS!*

≳ UHNNN ≲ *SOMETHING* STREAKING ACROSS MY PATH--

--GRABBED MY CAPE AND *PULLING* ON IT--

--AS IF KNOWING IT'S *INFINITELY STRETCHABLE!*

GREAT KRYPTON! IN MERE SECONDS IT'S YANKED MY CAPE *THOUSAND'S* OF MILES INTO SPACE!

WHO CAN BE SO *SUPER-STRONG* AND *SUPER-FAST*?

-UHNNN- THE CAPE'S SUDDENLY SNAPPED BACK INTO SHAPE LIKE A COLOSSAL RUBBER-BAND--

--AND THE *SUPER-RECOIL* EFFECT--

--IS CATAPULTING ME *OUT OF THIS WORLD!*

WHAT A *BREAK!* *SUPERMAN'S* HOT ON OUR TAILS--

--WHEN ALL OF A SUDDEN, HE TAKES OFF AFTER SOMEBODY ELSE!

CAPE'S SHRUNK ITSELF BACK TO NORMAL--

--BUT THE TREMENDOUS *MOMENTUM* IS SLINGSHOTING ME OUT OF THE *SOLAR SYSTEM!*

SHOOTING BY *SATURN--!*

AT THIS SPEED I WON'T BE ABLE TO TURN MYSELF AROUND TILL I PASS *URANUS!*

HAW! THEY SAID IT COULDN'T BE DONE!

WE PULLED OFF A HEIST IN *SMALLVILLE* AND *GOT AWAY WITH IT!*

ALL THAT STUFF ABOUT THE TOWN BEIN' *CRIME-PROOF* WAS A LOTTA BALONEY!

*B*UT WHAT OF THE *BLURRED FIGURE* JUST ABOVE THE COPTER'S WHIRLING *BLADE*-- A FIGURE WHIRLING AT SUPER-SPEED IN THE *OPPOSITE* DIRECTION?

HEYY! WHY WE LOSIN' ALTITUDE?

THE BLADE'S *SLOWING DOWN!*

THIS BIRD'S FALLIN' LIKE A *DEAD DUCK!*

CRIPES! THERE GOES OUR *PROPELLER!*

10

WE'RE *ALL* DEAD DUCKS!

WE WOULDA BEEN BETTER OFF IF *SUPERMAN* CAUGHT US!

PLUMMETING TOWARD THE EARTH, THE COPTER CROOKS LOSE CONSCIOUSNESS...

...AND REGAIN IT MOMENTS LATER ON THE GROUND...

WHAT HAPPENED? I THOUGHT WE WERE *GONERS!*

HOW'D WE END UP *HERE*--SAFE AND SOUND...

...AND *HANDCUFFED?*

YOU'RE ALL UNDER ARREST FOR ATTEMPTED BANK ROBBERY!

POLICE CHIEF PARKER--? I THOUGHT HE'D *RETIRED!*

NO WAY THAT OLD GEEZER COULD HAVE DONE *THIS!*

MAYBE *SUPERMAN* DOUBLED BACK AND NABBED US AFTER ALL!

I WOULD HAVE-- BUT THAT MYSTERIOUS "CAPE- STRETCHER" BEAT ME TO IT!

I RETURNED FROM SPACE JUST IN TIME TO SEE HIS *BLURRED SHAPE* SPEED AWAY FROM THE SCENE...DISAPPEAR FROM SIGHT!

I WONDER...IS THIS THE *EXPLANATION* FOR *SMALLVILLE'S CHARMED LIFE?*

HAS THE TOWN BEEN UNDER THE PROTECTION OF A *SECRET GUARDIAN* ALL THESE YEARS--

--A *GUARDIAN* WITH POWERS EQUAL...OR EVEN *GREATER*... THAN MY OWN?

11

PART TWO "EXIT THE GUARDIAN..."

I CAN'T IMAGINE *WHY* I PASSED OUT BEFORE, PETE...

BUT I MAY DO IT *AGAIN* IF YOU TELL ME A *75-YEAR-OLD* POLICE CHIEF *SINGLE-HANDEDLY* BROUGHT DOWN A HELICOPTER AND CAPTURED THOSE CROOKS!

POLICE

IF ANYONE ELSE WAS INVOLVED, LANA... *I DIDN'T SEE IT!*

YOU'VE GOT TO ADMIT EVEN *SUPERMAN* HIMSELF COULDN'T HAVE DONE A BETTER JOB!

THAT'S *IT!* I BET *SUPERMAN IS HERE!*

I JUST REMEMBERED-- HE HAS A *PERSONAL INTEREST* IN THE *COPTER CROOKS!* LET'S FIND *CLARK!*

SEVERAL BLOCKS DOWN THE STREET...

WE'RE IN *LUCK!* LIKE I HOPED, CLARK BROUGHT THE MORNING EDITION OF THE *DAILY PLANET* DOWN FROM *METROPOLIS* WITH HIM!

SO WHAT'S THE *PLANET* SUPPOSED TO TELL US?

IT'LL CONFIRM A *RADIO BULLETIN* I HEARD LAST NIGHT... ABOUT HOW *SUPERMAN* NABBED ANOTHER *COPTER-GANG* IN *METROPOLIS!*

MAYBE HE'S HERE IN *SMALLVILLE* TO FOLLOW-UP ON THE CASE!

I'M READING IT--BUT CAN'T BELIEVE IT!

WEATHER

DAILY ⊕ PLANET

SPORTS

SUPERMAN FOILS MIDNIGHT BANK ROBBERY!

COPTER CROOKS ATTEMPT ANOTHER SAFE-JACKING

THIS PHOTO *PROVES* SUPERMAN WAS IN *METROPOLIS* LAST NIGHT AT 12 O'CLOCK!

YET--AT THE SAME TIME-- I SAW HIM *HERE* IN SMALLVILLE STOPPING THE EARTHQUAKE!

12

NOT EVEN *SUPERMAN* CAN BE IN TWO PLACES AT THE SAME TIME!

I *GOT* IT!

THE *ANSWER* JUST HIT ME... LIKE A TON OF--!

GOT TO CHECK IT OUT!

PETE ROSS-- COME *BACK*!

DON'T YOU PULL A *CLARK KENT* ON ME--AND *RUN AWAY*!

*T*HREE BLOCKS SOUTH, ONE BLOCK WEST, AND PETE ROSS IS FACE-TO-FACE WITH...

...THE *KENT* HOME! THE HOUSE WHERE *CLARK* WAS RAISED AS A BOY!

IF MY *HUNCH* IS ON THE BEAM... THE *PROOF* WILL BE *IN THERE*!

SINCE THE KINDLY *KENTS* PASSED AWAY, *I'M* THE ONLY OTHER PERSON ON EARTH WHO KNOWS ABOUT THE SECRET *SUPERBOY ROOMS* CLARK BUILT INTO THIS HOUSE FOR HIS MEMENTOS AND TROPHIES!

NOW *WHERE* IS THAT FIRST SECRET PANEL...?

HEYY--!

MOMENTS LATER, PETE FINDS HIMSELF LOCKED INSIDE THE *SECRET ROOM*...

SO MY HUNCH WAS *RIGHT!* IT'S *YOU* WHO SAVED *SMALLVILLE* FROM THE QUAKE LAST NIGHT--

--YOU WHO'S BEEN WATCHING OVER THE TOWN ALL THESE YEARS, PROTECTING THE PEOPLE IN IT--

YOU--

--A *SUPERBOY ROBOT!*

YES, PETER ROSS ...I AM ONE OF THE *ROBOTS* SUPERBOY BUILT YEARS AGO!

AND I SERVED HIM FAITHFULLY, TOO...UNTIL THE DAY HE TURNED INTO A *TREACHEROUS* FOE!

I CAN SEE BY YOUR FACE YOU DON'T *BELIEVE* ME... BUT YOU'LL THINK DIFFERENTLY AFTER YOU HEAR MY *STORY!*

IT BEGAN THE NIGHT BEFORE MY *MASTER* LEFT *SMALLVILLE* TO BEGIN HIS COLLEGE CAREER AT *METROPOLIS UNIVERSITY*...

"HE SUMMONED ME AND MY FELLOW-ROBOTS-- AND SAID HE HAD ONE LAST *MISSION* FOR US..."

ROBOTS, I'VE GIVEN YOU A *PRIORITY-ONE* COMMAND!

NOW *FOLLOW* ME!

"HE LED US MILLIONS OF MILES INTO SPACE--TOWARD THE BLAZING INFERNO OF THE *SUN*..."

14.

35

AS YOU KNOW, PETE ROSS, *SUPERBOY* FITTED US ROBOTS WITH SPECIAL EQUIPMENT TO SIMULATE ALL HIS *SUPER-POWERS--*

--BUT OUR ARTIFICIAL POWERS WERE SEVERELY *LIMITED* COMPARED WITH *HIS--*

"--WHICH IS WHY A FLIGHT INTO THE SUN COULDN'T HARM THE *MASTER--* BUT WOULD SURELY DESTROY *US...*"

"*ONE* AFTER THE OTHER, THE ROBOTS LOYALLY FOLLOWED HIM...UNTIL THE OVERWHELM-ING *HEAT* HAD *VAPORIZED* THEM INTO GASEOUS WINDS..."

"*I,* TOO, WOULD HAVE MET THE SAME DOOM... IF MY *LOGIC-CIRCUITS* HAD NOT BEEN FUNCTIONING SO WELL AT THAT MOMENT..."

THIS DOES NOT *COMPUTE!*

MASTER PROGRAMMED US TO CLASSIFY ANY BEING WHO KILLS OTHERS AS *EVIL!*

MASTER HAS KILLED ALL THE OTHER *SUPERBOY-ROBOTS!*

CONCLUSION... *MASTER* IS *EVIL!*

HIS COMMAND TO FLY INTO THE SUN WAS *EVIL!*

MY LOGIC-BANKS WILL NOT PERMIT ME TO TAKE ORDERS FROM AN *EVIL BEING!*

FROM THAT DAY FORWARD I BECAME AN *INDEPENDENT UNIT!*

SINCE MY *ORIGINAL PROGRAMMING ORDERS* WERE TO *PROTECT SMALLVILLE* IN *SUPERBOY'S* ABSENCE--

--I HAVE BEEN FUNCTIONING IN THAT *CAPACITY* EVER SINCE!

15

YET YOU'VE KEPT YOUR EXISTENCE A *SECRET* ALL THESE YEARS...

YES...TO AVOID ANOTHER *CLASH* WITH MY *MASTER!*

BUT NOW THAT HE HAS RETURNED TO *SMALLVILLE,* A BATTLE IS INEVITABLE!

ABRUPTLY...

YOUR *EYES*-- GLOWING *RED!* WHAT--

IT IS A SPECIAL *ALARM SYSTEM* I'VE EQUIPPED MYSELF WITH TO ALERT ME TO ANY EMERGENCY IN TOWN!

YOU WILL GAIN NOTHING BY ESCAPING WHILE I'M GONE, PETER ROSS!

I'LL FIND YOU IN TIME TO PREVENT YOUR EVER REVEALING MY SECRET!

A *SONIC BOOM* HAS CAUSED DAMAGE ALONG *MAIN STREET!*

A COMBINATION OF *SUPER-SPEED FRICTION* AND *HEAT VISION* WILL MEND THE WINDOWS AND FUSE THOSE GLASS FRAGMENTS BACK TOGETHER TOO FAST TO BE *SEEN!*

GOT YOU!

I FIGURED IF I CAUSED A *SONIC BOOM* HERE, THE DISTURBANCE WOULD FLUSH YOU OUT--

--WHOEVER YOU ARE!

16

AND WHEN THE *ACTION ACE'S* STEELY GRIP BRINGS THE SUPER-SPEEDING FIGURE TO A *HALT*...

GREAT KRYPTON! I-I...

ALMOST LIKE TALKING TO *YOURSELF*, MASTER?

CAN IT BE? *SUPERBOY ROBOT-6*-- STILL FUNCTIONING?

YEARS AGO YOU TRIED TO DESTROY ALL YOUR ROBOTS--

--BUT THANKS TO MY *SUPERIOR LOGIC*, I ALONE *SURVIVED!*

AND NOW, IT IS *YOU* WHO MUST BE ELIMINATED! FOR YOU ARE AN *EVIL BEING!*

SLOW DOWN, *SR 6*-- YOU'RE NOT MAKING *SENSE!*

BESIDES, YOU FORGET *YOUR* POWERS ARE NO MATCH FOR *MINE!*

AND *YOU* FORGET WITH WHAT EASE I CATAPULTED YOU INTO *SPACE!*

LET THIS BLOW SERVE AS A *REMINDER!*

WOK

I HAVE INCORPORATED MANY *IMPROVEMENTS* INTO YOUR ORIGINAL DESIGN, MASTER--

--SUCH AS *ENERGY-IMPLANTS* TO *BOOST* MY ARTIFICIAL POWERS TO *EQUAL* YOURS!

SO I SEE! OBVIOUSLY, YOU'VE ALSO MADE YOURSELF IMMUNE TO THE *POLLUTION EFFECT!* *

*RECENTLY, THE *MAN OF STEEL* WAS FORCED TO *RETIRE* ALL HIS *SUPERMAN ROBOTS* BECAUSE THE EARTH'S *POLLUTED* ATMOSPHERE WAS MAKING THEM *MALFUNCTION!* -- Editor

17

AMONG THE ASTONISHED SMALLVILLE CITIZENS GAZING UPON THE BIZARRE SHOWDOWN-- LANA LANG AND CHIEF PARKER...

HOW CAN THIS BE HAPPENING?!-- SUPERMAN VS. SUPERBOY!

IT'S LIKE THE PRESENT AT WAR WITH THE PAST!

BUT I HAD TO DISPOSE OF YOU, SR-6! YOU ROBOTS WERE SUPERBOY-SUBS-- AND I WAS BECOMING A SUPERMAN!

YOUR MOTIVATIONS DO NOT MATTER! MY LOGIC BANKS HAVE CONCLUSIVELY COMPUTED THAT YOU ARE EVIL!

YEARS AGO, A BLOW LIKE THAT WOULD HAVE SHATTERED ME TO SCRAP-- BUT NOW IT DOES NOT EVEN SCRATCH MY SYNTHETIC SKIN!

SR-6 HAS NOT ONLY TURNED HIMSELF INTO A FORMIDABLE FOE--

--HE'S BECOME AS INDESTRUCTIBLE AS I AM!

BUT SINCE HIS LOGIC DICTATES HE MUST DISPOSE OF ME-- I'VE GOT NO CHOICE BUT TO USE LOGIC TO ELIMINATE HIM!

GOLL-LEE! DIDJA SEE THAT?

NEVER THOUGHT IT'D EVER HAPPEN!

THAT ROBOT SLUGGED SUPERMAN CLEAR OUTA SIGHT!

18

39

ALL *EVIL BEINGS* MUST BE *ELIMINATED!*

HE SUDDENLY TOOK OFF LIKE A SHOT!

WHERE'S HE GOING?

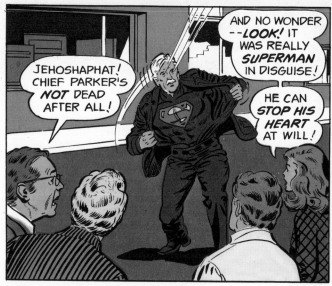

JEHOSHAPHAT! CHIEF PARKER'S *NOT* DEAD AFTER ALL!

AND NO WONDER--*LOOK!* IT WAS REALLY *SUPERMAN* IN DISGUISE!

HE CAN *STOP HIS HEART* AT WILL!

WHAT'S BEEN GOIN' ON HERE? WHAT'S ALL THIS *COMMOTION* ABOUT?

IT'S QUITE A STORY, CHIEF PARKER!

WHAT A CLEVER STUNT! *SUPERMAN* MUST'VE FLOWN BACK INTO TOWN AT *SUPER-SPEED* TO BORROW A POLICE UNIFORM AND DISGUISED HIMSELF AS *CHIEF PARKER!*

AND AS A PAIR OF *TELESCOPIC EYES* FOLLOWS THE *SUPERBOY* ROBOT SPEEDING SUNWARD...

SR-6 MUST HAVE "SHORTED" A CIRCUIT...MADE HIMSELF *VULNERABLE!* HE'S FINALLY FOLLOWING HIS FELLOW ROBOTS INTO *OBLITERATION!*

BY CONVINCING THE ROBOT HE HAD DONE SOMETHING *EVIL,* HIS COMPUTERIZED *LOGIC* DID THE REST--JUST AS I FIGURED!

THAT NIGHT--AFTER *PETE* HAS LEFT THE *KENT HOUSE* EXACTLY AS HE FOUND IT...

...AND WITHOUT THEIR *SECRET GUARDIAN* WATCHING OVER THEM, THE PEOPLE OF *SMALLVILLE* WILL HAVE TO BECOME SELF-RELIANT AGAIN, LIKE OTHER TOWNS!

LOOKS LIKE THINGS TURNED OUT FOR THE BEST--

--EXCEPT FOR *ONE THING, PETER ROSS* AND *CLARK KENT!*

BOTH OF YOU WERE *MISSING* WHILE ALL THE EXCITEMENT WAS GOING ON TODAY...

...WHICH LEADS ME TO BELIEVE *BOTH* OF YOU ARE HIDING *SECRETS!*

AND *SOMEDAY* I'M *GOING* TO FIND OUT *WHAT* THEY ARE!

THE END

PRIOR to its tragic and violent destruction, there lived on Superman's home planet of Krypton a race of people possessing a cultural and scientific sophistication far in advance of that of Earth. Capital punishment had been abolished by the Kryptonians, who introduced an alternative: imprisonment in artificial satellites orbiting the home planet. The convicted criminal was placed in a state of suspended animation by a special gas, and a shard of a crystalline substance which possessed the power of cleansing evil from their minds was placed near their heads. This system was replaced after a discovery by Superman's father, Jor-El. He called it 'The Phantom Zone'.

By means of a ray projector, Jor-El could transmit matter into a weird twilight dimension distantly connected with our own. The law-breakers of Krypton were now turned into living phantoms, unable to communicate with the world the were once a part of. They could see but not touch, hear but not speak. Inside the grim phantom world they required no sleep, food or air. The felons simply existed in a limbo state – a punishment the Kryptonian council considered to be the ultimate deterrent. Once a phantomised inmate had served his sentence, the Phantom Zone projector could again be used to release the hopefully reformed prisoner back into the real world.

The first time that Superman found out anything about the Phantom Zone was during his days as Superboy, when he lived in the town of Smallville with his adopted parents, Jonathan and Martha Kent. The now-classic story, "The Phantom Superboy" (*Adventure Comics No. 283*), related how a large metal box fell from the sky to crash into a desert in New Mexico. As fate would have it, the landing was witnessed by a Professor Lang, father of Lana Lang, who was on an archaeological expedition. He contacted Superboy, for the box could not apparently be opened by earthly means, and the young Boy of Steel used his super-strength to open the box. Superboy found to his surprise that the contents were from his home planet, Krypton. A note explained that the objects enclosed were highly dangerous. A 'thought helmet' found in the box activated a taped voice which gave a description of the uses of the contents, including a Phantom Zone projector. So intrigued was he by the discovery of the Kryptonian artifacts, Superboy failed to notice a desert lizard brush against the black button of the Zone device. It immediately activated, bathing Superboy in its ray and sending him into the Phantom Zone. Eventually he was freed, and another part of the Super-legend was created.

In later tales, Superman discovered that there were still criminals alive in the zone. Luckily for them, their disembodied, ghost-like state enabled them to escape the doom which had killed the other inhabitants of Krypton. It has never been revealed exactly how many criminals still reside in the zone, but they include:

JAX-UR has been described as 'The worst villain in the zone'. Once he had been an established member of the scientific community, until an experimental rocket he was working on proved faulty. It collided with, and destroyed an inhabited moon of Krypton. His infamous deed earned him a life sentence in the Phantom Zone.

> BUT AS THE NEXT CASE IS CALLED...
>
> I AM **PHANTOM ZONE** PRISONER, **JAX-UR**! I AM UNDER A LIFE-SENTENCE, BUT I APPEAL TO THE BOARD FOR MY RELEASE!
>
> NO! **JAX-UR** IS THE WORST TROUBLE-MAKER IN THE ZONE! HIS CRIME WAS THE MOST MONSTROUS OF ALL!

KRU-EL was a cousin of Superman's father Jor-El, but far from being an upstanding citizen. Almost as brilliant an inventor as his close relative, he chose to flaunt the law by creating an arsenal of destructive super-weapons. It was Jor-El who put an end to his short-lived criminal life and Kru-El was sentenced to a thirty five year spell in the timeless dimension.

GENERAL ZOD, seen in the Superman movies, created an army of imperfect bizarro-like duplicates of himself and launched an attack on Fort Rozz, the main centre of defence on Krypton. Zod attempted to sweep away the elected rulers of his planet and to substitute himself. Unluckily for the would-be dictator and his weirdo troops, the Kryptonian armed forces crushed his revolt and eventually captured him. His punishment was a sentence of forty years separated from reality in the Phantom Zone.

DR. XADU was transmitted into the zone for breaking Kryptonian laws whilst conducting experiments in the forbidden art of suspended animation. His subjects could not be woken from their state of perpetual sleep; Xadu paid the price with a thirty year sentence.

PROFESSOR VAKOX conducted experiments with a 'life force' chemical compound which he poured into the Great Lake of Krypton, creating a ferocious many headed lizard monster. Since the Science Council of his planet determined the lake would be contaminated for up to fifty years, his sentence was of a similar duration.

FAORA HU-UL operated a grisly concentration camp where she tormented, tortured and finally murdered twenty three citizens. For this ghastly transgression of the law she was despatched to the zone for a total of three hundred years – the only sentence longer than that of Jax-Ur.

The above names are some of the most diehard criminals that Krypton ever had to deal with, though there is one person in the zone who was placed there not for a crime, but to save his life. His name is MON-EL, and he had been accidentally lead poisoned. Since there is no illness in the Phantom Zone, all Superboy could do was to send him there until a cure could be found. The wait was worthwhile for Mon-El, for one thousand years later, the poisoning was cured by members of The Legion Of Super-Heroes in the thirtieth century.

Although there is no longer a planet Krypton, there still exists a Phantom Zone Appeal Board in the bottle city of Kandor, the function of which is to listen to appeals for release once every year. Superman is able to see inside the zone without actually entering by means of a zone-ophone which can pinpoint every inhabitant of the prison dimension. But it will be a long time yet before many of these imprisoned felons will find escape from the timeless Phantom Zone.

> ONE DAY, IN **SUPERMAN'S** ARCTIC **FORTRESS OF SOLITUDE** AS HE TESTS AN AMAZING NEW INVENTION WHILE **SUPERGIRL** WATCHES...
>
> CAN YOU HEAR ME, **SUPERMAN!**
>
> YES, **MON-EL!** WONDERFUL! MY **ZONE-OPHONE** WORKS! I CAN COMMUNICATE WITH **PHANTOM ZONE** PRISONERS...

SUPER-VISION TEST!

Uh-oh! It looks very much as though Mr Mxyzptlk has escaped from the fifth dimension again! He's always confusing the issue with his tricks and jokes. These two pictures of the J.L.A. actually started out the same, but this pesky creature has changed 15 things in the second picture! You really will need to put your super-vision to the test to find the subtle changes... but you'll be pleased to hear that before we tricked Mr Mxyzptlk in to saying his name backwards (he's safely back in the fifth dimension now!) we persuaded him to tell us exactly what he'd changed – so you'll find the answers at the bottom of the page!

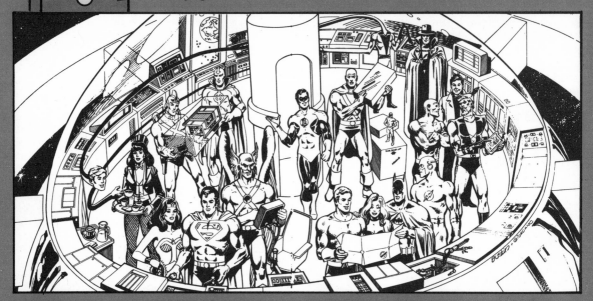

Flash's chest insignia different; sandwiches missing from the tray on the table in front of Zatanna; Plastic Man's foot missing; planet on rear screen has moved; Superman's belt different; Zatanna's bow-tie different; 'secret' label missing from document held by Batman; stripe on Red Tornado's leg missing; box beneath Atom is upside down; paper missing from Green Arrow's clipboard; star missing from Wonder Woman's tiara; no 'coffee' in Plastic Man's cup; extra star in sky (top left); artists' names reversed; Green Arrow's cap feather missing.

AS SUPERMAN STREAKS OFF INTO THE VELVET DARKNESS...

GREEN LANTERN OF TERRA! HEED MY *PLEA!*

ARCHON Z'GMORA, THE GREEN LANTERN OF *CYGNUS?*

I REQUIRE YOUR *ASSISTANCE,* MY BROTHER GREEN LANTERN!

PLEASE DO NOT *DELAY...* I MUST BE *RESCUED* BEFORE IT IS TOO LATE!

USE YOUR *POWER RING!* SURELY IT MUST--

MY RING IS *DESTROYED* ...MY POWER *GONE!* WERE IT NOT FOR THE NATURAL *TELEPATHIC ABILITIES* OF ALL CYGNIANS, I WOULD NOT BE ABLE TO SUMMON YOU!

WITH EVERY PASSING MOMENT, MY LIFE *EBBS*... WITH EVERY SECOND'S HESITATION, I COME CLOSER TO *FINALITY!*

I HAVE TO *RENEW* MY RING'S ENERGY!

BEING ON *MONITOR DUTY,* I DIDN'T THINK I'D NEED A FRESH *24-HOUR* SUPPLY OF POWER!

HURRY! ALREADY THE FABRIC THAT BINDS ME DISPERSES...

FOR A BRIEF MOMENT, GREEN LANTERN STARES SILENTLY AT THE BATTERY OF POWER. THEN, HE RECITES A *SOLEMN OATH...*

IN BRIGHTEST DAY, IN BLACKEST NIGHT, NO EVIL SHALL ESCAPE MY SIGHT! LET THOSE WHO WORSHIP EVIL'S MIGHT, BEWARE MY POWER-- GREEN LANTERN'S LIGHT!

AND THEN...

STRANGE! ARCHON'S NEVER BEEN ALL THAT *FRIENDLY* WITH ME... NOT SINCE THAT MATTER ON *ALTAIR-FOUR!*

SO, WHY SUMMON *ME?* WHY NOT *ZURON* OR *NORCHAVIUS?* THEY'RE HIS *FRIENDS!*

2

STILL, A QUICK *POWER-RING CHECK* PROVES HE *REALLY* IS ARCHON!

THE *UNIVERSE* HAS GONE WRONG, GREEN LANTERN OF TERRA!

WHAT IS IT, ARCHON? WHAT'S *WRONG*?

COME CLOSER AND YOU SHALL *SEE* THE PERIL THAT HAS PERVADED THIS DIMENSION LOST IN THE *TIME STREAM!*

I DON'T SEE A THING! WHAT'S GOING ON HERE?

THE *BLIND* NEVER SEE WHAT LOOMS BEFORE THEM, I SAID COME CLOSER-- *NOW!*

J...JORDAN...JORRDANNNN...

HUH? I WAS RIGHT! THIS SET-UP STINKS LIKE A THREE DAY-OLD *FLOUNDER!*

C'MON, ARCHON --SPILL IT BEFORE-- EH?

THAT *BOOT!?* ARCHON-- WHAT IN THE NAME OF *OA* IS GOING ON?

NOTHING IS TRANSPIRING. ALL HAS ALREADY *OCCURRED!*

THE *TRUE* CYGNIAN GREEN LANTERN HAS MUTTERED HIS *LAST*... HE IS NOW *DEAD*--

--JUST AS *YOU* SHALL SOON BE!

YOUR BODY-- QUIVERING... *CHANGING...*

GREAT GUARDIANS!!

BEFORE GREEN LANTERN'S ASTONISHED EYES, THE CYGNIAN'S FORM *EXPANDS* INTO ...

WE WHO ARE CALLED *N'GON* HAVE *SUMMONED* YOU HERE!

WE HAVE NEED OF YOUR *FORM* AND *FLESH!* WE REQUIRE YOUR *STRENGTH* AND *POWER!*

WE NEED ALL THAT AND *MORE*... AND TO ACQUIRE WHAT IS NEEDED, YOU MUST BE *DESTROYED!*

I THINK YOU'RE *FORGETTING* SOMETHING! AS LONG AS I WEAR MY *POWER RING*, I'VE GOT A CERTAIN *SAY* IN THESE MATTERS!

YOU HAVE *NO* SAY, TERRAN! N'GON DOES NOT GRANT THAT PRIVILEGE!

INDEED, ALL WE GRANT YOU IS -- *INSTANTANEOUS DEATH!*

ARGHHHH!

THE CYGNIAN *DESTROYED* HIS POWER RING BEFORE WE COULD LAY CLAIM TO IT!

BUT *YOU*, FOOL, WERE NOT GIVEN THAT CHANCE!

YOUR WEAPON WEARS WELL UPON OUR FINGER, FORMER GREEN LANTERN!

IT FITS AS IF WE WERE *BORN* TO IT!

HA! HA! HA! HA! HA! HA!

4

WE NOW STAND *CLOSER* TO SOLITARY EXISTENCE!

WITH YOUR *POWER RING,* N'GON CAN BE AS HE WAS!

TO BE *ONE* AGAIN... TO SOAR THROUGH THE STAR-STUDDED COSMOS AS A *SINGULAR ENTITY*...

THE VERY THOUGHT *BEGGARS* THE IMAGINATION!

"ONCE THIS ENTITY FLEW *ALONE*... UNTIL WE WERE CAUGHT WITHIN THE *ENERGY-TENDRILLS* OF A GREEN-GLOWING *SUN*...

"AT THAT MOMENT, THAT SOUL-SHATTERING INSTANT, N'GON BECAME *TWO!*

"...INSTANTLY *HATING* EACH OTHER'S EXISTENCE...

"WE STOOD *FACING* ONE ANOTHER...

"...WISHING EACH OTHER INSTANTANEOUS *DEATH!*

"BUT, WE WERE *EQUALS*... COMPLETELY MATCHED IN STRENGTH--

"THUS, OUR *SEPARATE* SEARCHES FOR *GREATER POWER* TOOK US TO THE MOST DISTANT SHORES OF THE ENDLESS UNIVERSE.

"*THIS* ENTITY CONCEIVED A MOST CUNNING SCHEME ... WE SOUGHT OUT BEINGS POSSESSING INCREDIBLE *POWER*...

"AND, ONE-BY-ONE, WE *STOLE* THAT POWER, MADE IT OURS!

"A DOZEN *BEINGS* PERISHED, EACH MAKING US STRONGER, EACH PREPARING THE WAY TO DESTROY THE *NEXT* MORE POWERFUL BEINGS!

5

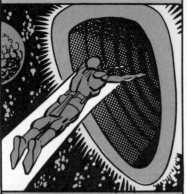

"IT WENT THUS FOR AN *AGE,* UNTIL THIS ENTITY SENSED THE EXISTENCE OF AN *ULTIMATE POWER!*

"A FORCE SO *AWESOME,* THAT WITH IT WE COULD EASILY DESTROY THE HATED *DOUBLE!*

"BUT, THAT FORCE WAS *TOO* STRONG! TO BATTLE IT, WE NEEDED TO ABSORB STILL *MORE* POWER ...AND SO WE FOUGHT THE GREEN LANTERN OF *CYGNUS!*

"BUT THE CYGNIAN KNEW HE WAS ABOUT TO TAKE HIS *FINAL BREATH*...

"...AND SO ORDERED HIS RING--THE SOURCE OF POWER *WE* DESPERATELY NEEDED--TO DESTROY ITSELF IN THE HEART OF AN *EXPLODING STAR!*

"STILL, WE DUPLICATED THE CYGNIAN'S FORM AND MEMORY, THEN LEARNED THROUGH HIM THE EXISTENCE OF *OTHER* RING-BEARERS!

"AND SO WE ATTACKED AND DEFEATED YOU...TOOK YOUR RING, *DUPLICATED* YOUR FORM AND MEMORIES--"

--AND NOW WE ARE PREPARED TO ATTACK AND DUPLICATE ONE *FINAL* BEING...

...AND HE WILL GIVE US THE POWER NECESSARY TO *DESTROY* MY BROTHER N'GON!

BUT FIRST, AS YOU RECITE YOUR *OATH OF ALLEGIANCE,* SO SHALL N'GON:

WITH POWER PRESENT IN LANTERN'S LIGHT, NO FORCE SHALL STAY MY HAND THIS NIGHT! LET THOSE WHO DO PREPARE TO FIGHT, DARE NO MAN CHALLENGE N'GON'S MIGHT!

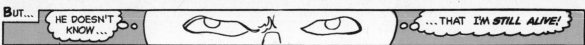

IT'S HERE ALL RIGHT-- AND IT'S ALREADY *KILLED* ANOTHER MEMBER OF THE LANTERN CORPS!

NOW IT'S AFTER *YOU!*

ME? WHY ME?

IT'S NO GOOD! SUPERMAN'S *FALLING* FOR IT.... HE DOESN'T REALIZE THAT GREEN LANTERN'S A *PHONY* RIGHT DOWN TO HIS IMITATION BOOTS!

HE'S GOT TO BE *WARNED...*

...AND SINCE I'M *HELPLESS* HANGING HERE IN MY ASTRAL FORM...

!WHEW! I DID IT! MY EMPTY BODY WAS JUST *WAITING* FOR ME TO TAKE IT OVER AGAIN!

I STILL DON'T FOLLOW YOU! IF THIS FORCE KILLED ANOTHER GREEN LANTERN, WHY DID IT LET *YOU* ESCAPE--

--AND WHY IS IT AFTER *ME?*

I...DIDN'T ESCAPE...I JUST *EVADED* ITS FIRST ATTACK...

...THEN TEMPORARILY *TRAPPED* IT WITH MY RING!

PLEASE, SUPERMAN-- COME *CLOSER...* AND YOU CAN SEE THE PERIL THAT HAS OVERTAKEN THIS *MAD* DIMENSION!

I...I DON'T KNOW. EVER SINCE I WAS *BROUGHT* HERE, I'VE FELT QUEASY... AS IF SOMETHING WERE *WRONG...*

SUPERMAN! GUARD YOURSELF!!

WHAT? *WHO--?*

WHEW! LANTERN'S RING CERTAINLY PACKS A *WALLOP!*

SPAK!

IT'S SENT ME SPINNING *OUT OF CONTROL!*

HAVE TO REMEMBER THE RING IS AS STRONG AS THE *WILL POWER* FOCUSED THROUGH IT!

AND, WITH THAT *ALIEN* WEARING IT, CHANCES ARE IT COULD MUSTER ENOUGH POWER TO EVEN *KILL ME!*

THAT IS *PRECISELY* WHAT N'GON INTENDS DOING!

I WILL *DESTROY* YOU, DUPLICATE YOUR *BODY AND POWER*--

RAK!

--THEN NOTHING, NOT EVEN THE *ULTIMATE ONE*, WILL STAND IN N'GON'S WAY!

--ONLY IF YOU *CATCH* ME, AND I DON'T *PLAN* ON LETTING THAT HAPPEN!

N'GON MAY HAVE INHERITED GREEN LANTERN'S *RING*, BUT HE ALSO INHERITED ITS ONE *WEAKNESS!*

PROBLEM IS, MY *TELESCOPIC VISION* CAN'T FIND IT *ANYWHERE!*

BUT THERE'S *GOT* TO BE SOME-- *HOLD IT!*

I WAS SEARCHING ACROSS HALF A *GALAXY*, AND I FAILED TO LOOK RIGHT UNDER MY *NOSE*--

--OR RATHER, *BEHIND MY BACK!*

56

BUT NOT EVEN THE *MAN OF STEEL'S* ASTONISHING SUPER-SPEED IS FASTER THAN--*THE SPEED OF THOUGHT...*

YOU MAY HAVE KNOWN THIS RING'S WEAKNESS, SUPERMAN, BUT I KNOW *YOURS!*

AND WHERE *MINE* MERELY DETERS ME, *YOURS* CAN *KILL YOU!*

GREAT *RAO! KRYPTONITE!*

A *WORLD* OF KRYPTONITE, SUPERMAN -- MORE OF THAT *KILLING* RADIATION THAN YOU HAVE EVER SUFFERED *BEFORE!*

SLOWLY, IT WILL INSINUATE ITS *POISONS* THROUGH YOUR PREVIOUSLY INVULNERABLE FLESH --

--AND THEN WHEN YOU CAN DO NOTHING MORE-- *YOU WILL DIE!*

BUT, BEFORE YOU DO, I WILL *TAP* INTO YOUR BEING...AND *DUPLICATE* YOUR POWERS AND PRESENCE!

CLOSE BY...

SUPERMAN'S ALREADY TURNING *GREEN* FROM THE KRYPTONITE POISONING, AND I'M *HELPLESS* JUST STANDING HERE WITH-OUT MY RING...

HELPLESS? NO-- JUST *POWERLESS!* BEING WITHOUT MY RING DOESN'T MEAN I CAN'T DO *SOMETHING!*

I'M *NOT* GOING TO LET N'GON JUST CALLOUSLY *MURDER* SUPERMAN--

--NOT EVEN IF IT *COSTS* MY LIFE TO STOP HIM!

N'GON! YOU'VE TAKEN ON MY POWER RING, YOU'VE BATTLED AGAINST SUPERMAN'S POWERS--

--BUT LET'S SEE HOW YOU FARE AGAINST A *COMMON ROCK!*

LOOK AT ME, SUPERMAN, MY *DEATH-STARE* ONCE MORE WELLS UP WITHIN ME... MY POWER IS NOW READY TO *REACH OUT AND DESTROY!!*

LOOK AT ME, YOU KRYPTONIAN CLOWN -- *AARGH!*

THOK!

UNHH...

I THINK YOU'VE *FORGOTTEN* SOMETHING -- SUPERMAN ISN'T *ALONE!*

HE *MAY* AS WELL BE, TERRAN!

WITHOUT YOUR RING -- YOU ARE *INCAPABLE* OF DOING A THING!

NOT QUITE TRUE, N'GON! LANTERN *DISTRACTED* YOU, AND WITHOUT YOUR *WILL POWER* FORMING THE KRYPTONITE, IT JUST *FADED* AWAY!

Y-YOU?!

THAT'S RIGHT...THE ONE YOU SAID WAS AS GOOD AS *DEAD!*

I *DIDN'T* BELIEVE IT WHEN YOU SAID IT--

--I *CERTAINLY* DON'T BELIEVE IT NOW!

SWOOOOOOOMMM

I GUESS THAT'S *THAT!*

YOU'RE WRONG, SUPERMAN -- YOU HAVEN'T EVEN *BEGUN!*

AS LONG AS HE WEARS MY RING, IT WILL *AUTOMATICALLY PROTECT* HIM FROM HARM!

HE SHOULD BE ROCKETING BACK HERE ANY SECOND!

N'GON KNOWS HE CAN'T WIN, HE'D BE A FOOL TO--

WELL, HE NEVER SAID HE WAS BRIGHT, DID HE? *LOOK!*

I APOLOGIZE, LANTERN, YOU WERE RIGHT!

ALL RIGHT, N'GON, WHAT'S IT GOING TO TAKE TO *KEEP* YOU DOWN?

14

58

MORE THAN YOU CAN MUSTER, SUPERMAN!

WATCH OUT FOR HIS **EYES!** WHEN THEY **GLOW,** HE'S READY TO ATTACK!

I'VE **NOTICED** THAT! JUST STAND BEHIND ME!

VERY **NOBLE,** SUPERMAN-- BUT MISTAKEN!

MY **DEATH- STARE** CAN DESTROY YOU BOTH WHERE YOU STAND!

--AND FRANKLY, YOU'RE **NOT** GETTING IT!

ONLY IF YOU GET THE CHANCE TO **USE** IT--

WITH THE **BURNING FORCE** OF A HUNDRED BLAZING SUNS, SUPERMAN'S INCREDIBLE **HEAT VISION** LASHES OUTWARD--

--BUT EVEN AS N'GON'S **STOLEN RING** AUTOMATI- CALLY FORMS A LIFE-SAVING SHIELD AROUND HIM...

I'VE TAKEN ABOUT AS MUCH OF THIS **NONSENSE** AS I'M WILLING TO!

WE'RE GETTING **OFF** THIS WORLD RIGHT NOW!

THIS SHOULD BE FAR ENOUGH INTO SPACE!

YOU DARE--

YOU MAY HAVE LANTERN'S **RING** TO PROTECT YOU, BUT I'VE GOT A LITTLE SOMETHING CALLED **SUPER-STRENGTH!**

SO LET'S SEE HOW **POWERFUL** THAT RING **REALLY** IS!

15

-- BECAUSE I DON'T BELIEVE YOU'LL *EVER* BE LEAVING THIS *TIMELESS* DIMENSION!

SAY, PAL, WHY THE *LONG FACE?* WE STOPPED N'GON, GOT BACK MY POWER RING...

STILL, BEFORE I WAS *YANKED* HERE, I WAS ABOUT TO *SAVE* A FALLING MAN!

I WAS SO *CLOSE*... I COULD ALMOST *TOUCH* HIM! THEN...

THAT'S SOMETHING I WOULDN'T WORRY ABOUT!

MOMENTS LATER, AFTER THE EMERALD PRISON CARRIES N'GON INTO AN *ETERNAL ORBIT*...

WE'RE IN A *TIME DIMENSION* ...ONE THAT MOVES AT A *DIFFERENT RATE* THAN OUR OWN!

C'MON, WHAT ARE YOU WAITING FOR? LET'S *GO!*

I STILL DON'T UNDER-STAND...

THIS DIMENSION MOVES MORE *SLOWLY* THAN OURS... SO ALL I HAD TO DO WAS *PINPOINT* THE PRECISE MOMENT YOU WERE PLUCKED FROM OUR TIME...

...AND SIMPLY ARRANGE FOR US TO *REAPPEAR* THERE A FRACTION OF A SECOND LATER!

WHUMP!

SEE? THE OLD RING HAS ITS *USES* AFTER ALL!

LANTERN, I *NEVER* DOUBTED THAT FOR ONE MOMENT!

- THE END -